PEARSON EDEXCEL INTERNATIONAL AS/A LEVEL

PHYSICS

Lab Book

Published by Pearson Education Limited, 80 Strand, London, WC2R 0RL.

www.pearsonglobalschools.com

Copies of official specifications for all Pearson Edexcel qualifications may be found on the website: https://qualifications.pearson.com

Text © Pearson Education Limited 2018
Designed by Tech-Set Ltd, Gateshead, UK
Edited by Stephanie White and Jane Read
Typeset by Tech-Set Ltd, Gateshead, UK
Original illustrations © Pearson Education Limited 2018
Cover design by Pearson Education Limited 2018

The right of Steve Adams and Keith Bridgeman to be identified as authors of this work has been asserted by them in accordance with the Copyright, Designs and Patents Act 1988.

First published 2018

25 24
10 9

British Library Cataloguing in Publication Data
A catalogue record for this book is available from the British Library
ISBN 9781292244754

A note from the Publishers: found on the website: www.edexcel.com
While the Publishers have made every attempt to ensure that advice on the qualification and its assessment is accurate, the official specification and associated assessment guidance materials are the only authoritative source of information and should always be referred to for definitive guidance. Pearson examiners have not contributed to any sections in this resource relevant to examination papers for which they have responsibility. Examiners will not use this resource as a source of material for any assessment set by Pearson.

Neither Pearson, Edexcel nor the authors take responsibility for the safety of any activity. Before doing any practical activity you are legally required to carry out your own risk assessment. In particular, any local rules issued by your employer must be obeyed, regardless of what is recommended in this resource. Where students are required to write their own risk assessments they must always be checked by the teacher and revised, as necessary, to cover any issues the students may have overlooked. The teacher should always have the final control as to how the practical is conducted.

Printed in Great Britain by Bell and Bain Ltd, Glasgow

CONTENTS

INTRODUCTION

Practical work is central to the study of physics. The International Advanced Subsidiary / Advanced Level (IAS / IAL) specification includes 16 core practical activities that link theoretical knowledge and understanding to practical scenarios. By completing the core practical activities, you will learn to:

- follow and interpret experimental instructions, covering a range of laboratory exercises throughout the course, with minimal help from your teacher
- manipulate apparatus, carry out all common laboratory procedures and use data logging (where appropriate)
- work sensibly and safely in the laboratory, paying due regard to health and safety requirements
- gain accurate and consistent results in quantitative exercises, and make the most of the expected observations in qualitative exercises

By the end of this course, you should be able to use a variety of apparatus and techniques to:

- design and carry out both the core practical activities and your own investigations
- collect data that can be analysed
- use data to draw valid conclusions.

Your knowledge and understanding of practical skills and activities will be assessed in all examination papers.

- Papers 1 and 2 (IAS), and 4 and 5 (IAL) will include questions based on practical activities, including novel scenarios.
- Paper 3 (IAS) and Paper 6 (IAL) will test your ability to plan practical work, including risk management and selection of apparatus.

Assessment for the Practical Skills Papers 3 and 6 will focus on three main areas:

- **Planning:** You will be expected to plan an experiment set by Pearson (but you will not need to carry it out).
- **Implementation and measurements:** You will be given details of an experiment carried out by an inexperienced student, and asked to comment on the investigation.
- **Processing results / Analysing:** You will need to analyse a set of experimental results.

The areas for assessment are outlined in the tables on pages 4 and 5. You may wish to tick off each element as you gain confidence. You can also refer to the Student Practical Guide, and the Appendix 10 in the specification: Uncertainties and practical work.

You will find answers and maths skills required for the practicals at the back of the book.

UNIT 1 (IAS): MATERIALS

1 Determine the acceleration of a freely-falling object

2 Use a falling-ball method to determine the viscosity of a liquid

3 Determine the Young modulus of a material

UNIT 2 (IAS): WAVES AND ELECTRICITY

4 Determine the speed of sound in air using a 2-beam oscilloscope, signal generator, speaker and microphone

5 Investigate the effects of length, tension and mass per unit length on the frequency of a vibrating string or wire

6 Determine the wavelength of light from a laser or other light source using a diffraction grating

UNIT 2 (IAS): ELECTRIC CIRCUITS

7 Determine the electrical resistivity of a material

8 Determine the e.m.f. and internal resistance of an electrical cell

UNIT 4 (IAL): FURTHER MECHANICS

9 Investigate the relationship between the force exerted on an object and its change of momentum

10 Use ICT to analyse collisions between small spheres

UNIT 4 (IAL): ELECTRIC AND MAGNETIC FIELDS

11 Use an oscilloscope or data logger to display and analyse the potential difference (p.d.) across a capacitor as it charges and discharges through a resistor

UNIT 5 (IAL): THERMODYNAMICS

12 Calibrate a thermistor in a potential divider circuit as a thermostat

13 Determine the specific latent heat of a phase change

14 Investigate the relationship between pressure and volume of a gas at fixed temperature

UNIT 5 (IAL): NUCLEAR DECAY

15 Investigate the absorption of gamma radiation by lead

16 Determine the value of an unknown mass using the resonant frequencies of the oscillation of known masses

Practical skills	Core practical							
Planning	1	2	3	4	5	6	7	8
Identify the apparatus required								
Consider the range and resolution of measuring instruments including Vernier calipers (0.1 mm) and micrometer screw gauge (0.01 mm)								
Discuss calibration of instruments, e.g. whether a meter reads zero before measurements are made								
Describe how to measure relevant variables using the most appropriate instrument and correct measuring techniques								
Identify and state how to control all other relevant variables to make it a fair test								
Discuss whether repeat readings are appropriate								
Identify health and safety issues and discuss how these may be dealt with								
Discuss how the data collected will be used								
Identify possible sources of uncertainty and/or systematic error and explain how these may be reduced or eliminated								
Comment on the implications of physics (e.g. benefits/risks) and on its context (e.g. social/environmental/historical)								
Implementation and measurement	1	2	3	4	5	6	7	8
Comment on the number of readings taken								
Comment on the range of measurements taken								
Comment on significant figures								
Check a reading that is inconsistent with other readings, e.g. a point that is not on the line of a graph – students may be shown a diagram of a micrometer that is being used to measure the diameter of a wire and asked to write down the reading to the correct number of significant figures								
Comment on how the experiment may be improved, possibly by using additional apparatus (e.g. to reduce errors) – examples may include using a set square to determine whether a ruler is vertical to aid the measurement of the extension of a spring								
Processing results	1	2	3	4	5	6	7	8
Perform calculations, using the correct number of significant figures								
Plot results on a graph using an appropriate scale								
Use the correct units throughout								
Comment on the relationship obtained from the graph								
Determine the relationship between two variables or determine a constant with the aid of a graph, e.g. by determining the gradient using a large triangle								
Suggest realistic modifications to reduce errors								
Suggest realistic modifications to improve the experiment								
Discuss uncertainties, qualitatively and quantitatively								
Determine the percentage uncertainty in measurements for a single reading using half the resolution of the instrument and from multiple readings using the half range								

Practical skills	Core practical							
Planning	9	10	11	12	13	14	15	16
Identify the most appropriate apparatus, giving details. These may include the range and resolution of instruments and/or relevant dimensions of apparatus (e.g. the length of string used for a pendulum)								
Discuss calibration of instruments, e.g. whether a meter reads zero before measurements are made								
Describe how to measure relevant variables using the most appropriate instrument(s) and techniques								
Identify and state how to control all other relevant variables to make it a fair test								
Discuss whether repeat readings are appropriate								
Identify health and safety issues and discuss how these may be dealt with								
Discuss how the data collected will be used.								
Analysis	9	10	11	12	13	14	15	16
Comment on how the experiment could have been improved, possibly by using additional apparatus (e.g. to reduce errors) – examples may include using set squares to measure the diameter of a cylinder and using a marker for timing oscillations								
Comment on the number of readings taken								
Comment on the range of measurements taken								
Comment on significant figures – you may be required to identify and/or round up any incorrect figures in a table of results								
Identify and/or amend units that are incorrect								
Identify and check a reading that is inconsistent with other readings, e.g. a point that is not on the line of a graph.								
Perform calculations, using the correct number of significant figures								
Plot results on a graph using an appropriate scale and units – the graph could be logarithmic in nature								
Use the correct units throughout								
Comment on the trend/pattern obtained								
Determine the relationship between two variables or determine a constant with the aid of the graph, e.g. by determining the gradient using a large triangle								
Use the terms precision, accuracy and sensitivity appropriately								
Suggest realistic modifications to reduce errors								
Suggest realistic modifications to improve the experiment								
Discuss uncertainties qualitatively and quantitatively								
Compound percentage uncertainties correctly								
Determine the percentage uncertainty in measurements for a single reading using **half** the resolution of the instrument **and** from multiple readings using the **half** range.								

CORE PRACTICAL 1:

DETERMINE THE ACCELERATION OF A FREELY-FALLING OBJECT

Procedure

1 Drop the object from rest and record the time taken, t, for:

   (a) the sphere to fall through the trap door

   (b) the dowel to pass through the light gate.

2 Repeat step **1** twice more and calculate the mean value of t for each method.

3 Measure and record the height, h, fallen by the object.

4 Vary the height and repeat steps **1–3**. You should take readings at at least six different heights.

5 Use half the range in your readings for t as the uncertainty in t. Calculate the percentage uncertainty in t.

6 For method **(b)**, you should measure the length of the dowel.

Learning tips

- Make sure that points plotted on a graph take up more than half of the available space on each scale. You do not always need to include the origin.
- Keep scales simple: one large square as 5, 10 or 20 is ideal. A scale where one large square represents 3 or 7 units (or similar) is very difficult to plot and can often lead to errors.
- Always consider whether the graph line should go through the origin.
- Straight lines should be drawn with the aid of a rule long enough to cover the full length of the line.
- Since the object is falling at constant acceleration, use the appropriate kinematics equation:

   (a) $s = ut + \frac{1}{2}at^2$ where $u = 0$, $a = g$, and $s = h$

     This can be rearranged to: $t^2 = \frac{2h}{g}$

     Comparison with $y = mx + c$ shows that plotting t^2 against h should give a straight line passing through the origin with gradient $\frac{2}{g}$.

   (b) $v^2 = u^2 + 2as$ where $u = 0$, $a = g$, and s is h

     Therefore: $v^2 = 2gh$

     Comparison with $y = mx + c$ shows that plotting v^2 against h should give a straight line passing through the origin with gradient $2g$.

Objectives

- To measure the acceleration due to gravity, g, of an object falling freely and to consider the following alternative methods:

   (a) object falling through a trap door

   (b) object falling through a light gate

Equipment

- metre rule or tape measure with millimetre resolution

For **(a)**:

- steel sphere
- electronic timer
- electromagnet to retain steel sphere
- trap door switch
- clamp and stand
- low voltage power supply

For **(b)**:

- falling object, such as a dowel with 2 cm diameter, 10 cm long
- means to guide dowel through light gate
- light gate and datalogger

⚠ Safety

- Make sure the stand cannot topple over by clamping it securely.
- Keep hands and face away from the falling objects.
- Turn off the electromagnet between 'drops' so that it doesn't overheat and cause burns.

Results

1 Use this space to record your results for method **(a)**.

2 Use this space to record your results for method **(b)**. Use your value for the length of the dowel to calculate the mean speed, v, of the dowel as it passes through the light gate.

Analysis of results

1   For method **(a)**, plot a graph of t^2 (*y*-axis) against *h* (*x*-axis) and draw a line of best fit.

2   Calculate the gradient, *m*, of the line of best fit. Use this value to calculate a value for *g* where $g = \frac{2}{m}$.

3 For method **(b)**, plot a graph of v^2 (y-axis) against h (x-axis) and draw a line of best fit.

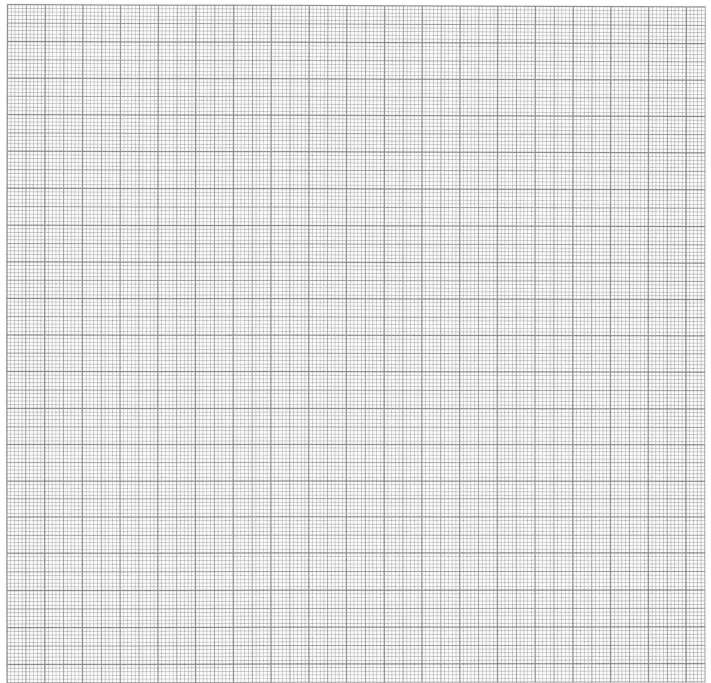

4 Calculate the gradient, m, of the line of best fit. Use this value to calculate a value for g, where $g = \dfrac{m}{2}$.

5 The percentage uncertainty (%U) in t^2 is twice that in t. Use this to draw error bars onto your graph for method **(a)** – in the y-direction only. You can use a typical mid-range value to calculate uncertainties – you do not need to work out a separate error bar for each value. Draw a new line of best fit and use this to calculate the %U in your value for g.

6 Calculate the percentage difference (%D) between your value and the accepted value of g (9.81 ms^{-2}) and comment on the accuracy of method **(a)**.

Questions

1 Describe an advantage of using light gates in this experiment.

....

....

....

....

2 Discuss the effect of air resistance on your value for g.

....

....

....

....

....

3 Explain why the graph should be a straight line.

....

....

....

....

Procedure

1 Weigh each ball, measure its radius, r, and hence calculate its density, ρ.

2 Place three rubber bands around the tube. Position the highest band at a level below the surface of the washing-up liquid: the ball must be travelling at terminal velocity when it reaches this band. Place the remaining two bands far enough apart to allow you to measure two reasonable time intervals. This will enable you to measure the terminal velocity twice for each falling ball.

3 Release the first ball into the washing-up liquid. Start the timer when the ball passes the highest rubber band. Use the lap timer facility to record the time taken, t_1, for the ball to fall to the middle rubber band. Stop the timer when the ball passes the lowest rubber band; this is t_2. Adjust the position of the rubber bands if your first test is not suitable.

4 Once you are happy with the position of the rubber bands, measure the distance, d_1, between the highest and middle rubber bands. Then, measure the distance, d_2, between the highest and lowest bands.

5 Repeat step **3** at least three times for each ball.

Learning tip

- Position your eyes level with the rubber bands when starting and stopping the timer.
- Try to develop a good technique for measuring the time, so you are consistent. For example, if you take your first measurement as the bottom of the ball crosses the top of the band, make sure you take every measurement at this point. You should also measure your distances from this point.

Results (Use this space to record your results.)

Equipment

- stop clock or timer
- rubber bands to mark distances
- metre rule
- micrometer screw gauge
- long tube made of transparent material filled with liquid – supported so it stays vertical
- spherical objects of various diameters
- magnet (optional)

⚠ Safety

- Washing-up liquid spills are very slippery and must be cleared up at once. Have paper towels to hand.
- Secure the tube so that it cannot topple over and have it at a level that does not require anyone to have to stand on a stool or table.
- If you use mineral oil or motor oil as the liquid avoid skin contact with it and the oily metal balls.

Results (continued)

Analysis of results

1   For each diameter, calculate mean values for t_1 and t_2. Add these values to your results table.

2   Use d_1, d_2 and the mean values for t_1 and t_2 to calculate mean values for the terminal velocity of each ball. Add these values to your results table.

3   Use your answers to question **2** to calculate a mean value for the terminal velocity of all the balls.

4   Consider the spread in your repeated readings and use this to estimate the uncertainty in your mean values. This is usually half of the range.

Questions

1 Explain why you would not use light gates to measure the time.

....

....

....

....

2 Sometimes the balls fall close to the wall. Comment on the effect this will have on the measurements.

....

....

....

....

....

....

3 Use your answer to question **4** above to estimate the uncertainty in your value for the viscosity of the washing-up liquid.

....

....

....

....

....

....

....

....

....

....

....

....

....

....

....

....

Procedure

1 Fix the bench pulley at the end of the bench. Trap one end of the wire between the two wooden blocks and secure the blocks to the bench approximately 3 m from the pulley. Lay out the wire so that it passes over the pulley and attach the slotted mass hanger to the end. Measure the diameter, d, of the wire.

2 Lay the metre rule under the wire near the pulley and attach the sticky label to act as a length marker. Judge the length by looking vertically down, over the edge of the paper, at the scale of the metre rule. The set square will help you to do this accurately.

3 Measure the length of wire, L, from the wooden blocks to the edge of the paper.

4 Add a mass to the hanger and record the position of the marker against the metre rule. Calculate the extension, x.

5 Repeat step **4**, adding one mass at a time and recording the extension for each mass.

Learning tips

- You might notice significant creep occurring at higher loads. This indicates that the elastic limit of the wire has been exceeded. It is important to use a long length of wire, as the extension will only be small before creep sets in.
- If you use weights of 0.5 N, you will be able to take more readings before the elastic limit is exceeded.

Objectives

- To take measurements of a long wire to determine the Young modulus for copper

Equipment

- metre rule
- micrometer screw gauge
- small piece of sticky label or similar, to mark position on wire
- 90° set square
- 3.1 m length of 36 swg copper wire
- two wooden blocks and clamp to secure one end of the wire
- bench pulley
- slotted masses up to 600 g and hanger

⚠ Safety

- Wear eye protection and avoid overloading the wire as it may snap and cause injury.
- Put a catch box filled with crumpled paper or bubbled plastic below the hanging masses to keep your feet out of the drop zone.
- Do not exceed the maximum load as advised by your teacher.

Results (Use this space to record your results.)

Analysis of results

1   Plot a graph of mass added against extension.

2   Measure the gradient of the straight portion of the graph and use this to calculate the Young modulus for the copper.

Questions

1 Explain why a long wire is most suitable for this experiment.

....

....

....

....

2 Describe a good technique for measuring the diameter of the wire.

....

....

....

....

....

3 Explain why a value with two significant figures is appropriate for the Young modulus of the wire.

....

....

....

....

....

4 Research a value for the Young modulus of copper and comment on your results, using an appropriate format to cite your research.

....

....

....

....

....

....

....

....

....

CORE PRACTICAL 4:
DETERMINE THE SPEED OF SOUND IN AIR USING A 2-BEAM OSCILLOSCOPE, SIGNAL GENERATOR, SPEAKER AND MICROPHONE

Procedure

1   The oscilloscope will display on two traces the signal fed to the loudspeaker and the signal received by the microphone. As the distance between the microphone and the speaker is increased, the phase of the signals will vary and the traces on the screen will move past each other.

2   Place the microphone next to the oscilloscope and place the speaker about 50 cm away, facing the microphone. Turn on the signal generator and set it to about 4 kHz. Adjust the oscilloscope to show the microphone signal with about three cycles on the screen.

3   Connect the signal generator output to the second oscilloscope input (as well as the speaker) and adjust the controls to display three cycles of this signal.

4   Adjust the spacing on the screen and the distance between the speaker and the microphone so that the bottom of one trace is just level with the top of the other.

5   Adjust the separation so that a trough on the top trace coincides exactly with a peak on the lower trace. Use a metre rule to measure the distance between the microphone and speaker.

6   Move the speaker away from the microphone and observe one trace moving relative to the other. Move the speaker until the trace has moved exactly one cycle – the troughs and peaks should just touch again. Record the new distance between the microphone and speaker. The difference between the two distances is one wavelength.

7   Repeat step **6** several times, moving the speaker further away from the microphone and recording the distance each time the peaks of one trace coincide with the troughs of the other.

8   Calculate a mean value for the wavelength of the sound, giving your answer to at least two significant figures.

9   Use one of the traces to determine the frequency of the sound. (You will achieve a greater resolution by this method than by using the scale on the signal generator.) Give your answer to at least three significant figures.

10 Use the scale on the signal generator to halve the frequency and repeat steps **4–9**. You might need to increase the separation beyond 1 m.

11 If you have time, repeat the whole experiment at much higher and much lower frequencies and observe the effect.

Learning tips

- This experiment is reasonably straightforward if you are familiar with manipulating the controls of an oscilloscope. Spend some time practising until you are confident setting up a trace from which you can take measurements.

- The set-up depends on the local circumstances, so you should try things out for yourself, using the instructions as a framework.

Objectives

- To use appropriate instrumentation to measure a sound signal

Equipment

- two metre rules
- leads
- signal generator with loudspeaker
- oscilloscope with 2-beam facility and microphone connected to one input

⚠ Safety

- The electromotive forces are small and electric currents negligible.
- Avoid using high volumes and frequencies that cause discomfort.
- If you have a hearing problem or wear a hearing aid tell your teacher as there may be uncomfortable effects at certain frequencies.
- Follow the usual electrical precautions for mains apparatus, including a visual inspection of the supply lead.

CORE PRACTICAL 4:
DETERMINE THE SPEED OF SOUND IN AIR USING A 2-BEAM OSCILLOSCOPE,
SIGNAL GENERATOR, SPEAKER AND MICROPHONE

SPECIFICATION
REFERENCE

2.3.38

Results (Use this space to record your results.)

Analysis of results

1 Multiply your values for wavelength and frequency to obtain a value for the speed of sound for each of the frequencies used. Hence, find a mean value and percentage difference for the speed of sound.

2 Estimate the uncertainty in your mean value for the wavelength of the sound (calculated in step **8**).

3 Estimate the uncertainty in your measurement of the frequency of the sound (calculated in step **9**).

4 Use the uncertainties from your measurements to calculate the percentage uncertainty in your individual values for the speed of sound.

CORE PRACTICAL 4:
DETERMINE THE SPEED OF SOUND IN AIR USING A 2-BEAM OSCILLOSCOPE, SIGNAL GENERATOR, SPEAKER AND MICROPHONE

SPECIFICATION REFERENCE

2.3.38

Questions

1 Comment on the sources of uncertainty in this investigation.

....

....

....

....

2 Compare your percentage difference and your percentage uncertainties, and comment on your results.

....

....

....

....

3 When the traces have moved past each other by one full cycle, the speaker has moved one wavelength. Explain this.

....

....

....

....

4 Explain why 4 kHz is a suitable frequency for this experiment.

....

....

CORE PRACTICAL 5:
INVESTIGATE THE EFFECTS OF LENGTH, TENSION AND MASS PER UNIT LENGTH
ON THE FREQUENCY OF A VIBRATING STRING OR WIRE

SPECIFICATION
REFERENCE

2.3.43

Procedure

1 Attach one end of the 'string' to the vibration transducer. Pass the other end over the bench pulley and attach the mass hanger.

2 Add masses until the total mass is 100 g.

3 Turn on the signal generator to set the rubber oscillating. Vary the oscillating length by moving the vibration generator until resonance is observed.

Plan

In this investigation, you will be observing standing waves. These can occur at a variety of resonant frequencies. You will investigate the effect of the factors affecting these frequencies.

You might use a cathode ray oscilloscope to determine the exact frequency of the vibration generator.

Plan which variables you will test in this investigation and how you will carry it out. Your teacher will help you with the details if necessary.

Use this space to record your plan.

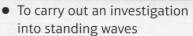

Objectives

- To carry out an investigation into standing waves
- To develop the skills to carry out further investigations

Equipment

- bench pulley
- slotted masses and hanger
- metre rule
- 2 m length of rubber 'string'
- vibration generator connected to a signal generator

⚠ Safety

- Rubber cord or string is less hazardous than using wire. If wire is used, eye protection should be worn.
- Visually check the mains plug, socket and lead for any damage before use.

Learning tip

- Your measurements will have greater resolution if you measure as large a length as possible, or as many half-wavelengths as possible.

CORE PRACTICAL 5:
INVESTIGATE THE EFFECTS OF LENGTH, TENSION AND MASS PER UNIT LENGTH ON THE FREQUENCY OF A VIBRATING STRING OR WIRE

SPECIFICATION REFERENCE

2.3.43

Results

1   Use this space to record your results.

2   Assess the uncertainties in your measurements and comment on whether they affect the reproducibility of your findings.

CORE PRACTICAL 5:
INVESTIGATE THE EFFECTS OF LENGTH, TENSION AND MASS PER UNIT LENGTH ON THE FREQUENCY OF A VIBRATING STRING OR WIRE

SPECIFICATION
REFERENCE

2.3.43

Analysis of results

Produce a graph of your results to show the relationships between the variables you identified and measured.

CORE PRACTICAL 5:
INVESTIGATE THE EFFECTS OF LENGTH, TENSION AND MASS PER UNIT LENGTH ON THE FREQUENCY OF A VIBRATING STRING OR WIRE

SPECIFICATION REFERENCE

2.3.43

Questions

1 Identify the major sources of uncertainty in your work.

....

....

....

....

2 Explain why you chose the variables you did.

....

....

....

....

....

3 Describe what you found difficult to get right and how you did get it right.

....

....

....

....

4 Research how a standing wave can be set up and used to determine a value for the speed of electromagnetic radiation. Use an appropriate format to cite any sources you use in your research.

....

....

....

....

....

....

....

....

....

....

SPECIFICATION REFERENCE

2.3.52

Procedure

1 Place the laser approximately 4 m away from a large wall and place the diffraction grating in front of it. Position the laser so that the beam will pass through the grating at normal incidence and meet the wall perpendicularly.

2 Measure the distance, *D*, between the grating and the wall.

3 Turn on the laser and identify the zero order maximum (straight through). Measure the distance, *s*, from the zero order maximum to the first-order maxima on either side. Calculate the mean of these two values. (Remember, the first order is the maximum produced according to $n = 1$ in the equation $n\lambda = d\sin\theta$.)

4 Measure *s* for increasing orders, calculating a mean value each time.

5 Repeat steps **1–4** using a diffraction grating with a different number of slits/mm.

Learning tip

- Make sure that the laser hits the wall at right angles.

Results (Use this space to record your results.)

CORE PRACTICAL 6:
DETERMINE THE WAVELENGTH OF LIGHT FROM A LASER OR OTHER LIGHT SOURCE USING A DIFFRACTION GRATING

SPECIFICATION REFERENCE

2.3.52

Results (continued)

Analysis of results

1 Since the angle is not small, you will need to calculate θ from your measurements of s and D. Calculate a mean θ value for each order.

2 Calculate a mean value for the wavelength of the laser light and compare this value with the accepted wavelength for a standard school red laser (635 nm).

Questions

1 State the advantages of using laser light in this experiment.

....

....

....

....

....

....

....

....

2 Explain why a metre rule is suitable for measuring the distance in this experiment.

....

....

....

....

....

....

3 Describe what the diffraction maxima would look like if a white laser was used (assuming such a thing was possible).

....

....

....

....

....

CORE PRACTICAL 7:
DETERMINE THE ELECTRICAL RESISTIVITY OF A MATERIAL

Procedure

1 Set up the apparatus as shown in Figure A. You will use the 4 mm plug at the free end of the second lead to make contact with different places on the wire.

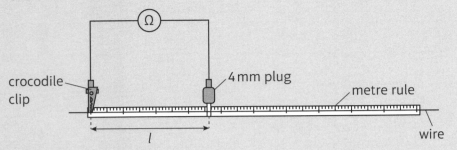

Figure A: Experimental set-up

2 Attach the crocodile clip to the wire, level with the 'zero' marker on the metre rule.

3 Place the 4 mm plug against the wire approximately 10 cm from the 'zero' end. You will need to press the plug firmly onto the wire to obtain a steady reading on the multimeter. Measure and record the resistance, R, and the length, l, of wire from the 'zero' end.

4 Move the plug along the wire in steps of 10 cm, and record R and l at each step.

5 Measure the diameter of the wire.

Results

1 Use this space to record your results.

Equipment

- 1.05 m of 34 swg constantan wire
- metre rule
- two leads, one with a crocodile clip on one end
- digital multimeter switched to the lowest ohms scale with both the leads plugged in
- micrometer screw gauge

 Safety

- Voltages and currents are small so there is no electric shock hazard.
- There is a risk of burns as the wire will get hot if not disconnected between readings.

2 Estimate the uncertainties in your measurements of R, l and the diameter of the wire.

Analysis of results

1 Plot a graph of R against l and draw a line of best fit.

2 Find the gradient, m, of your line of best fit.

3   Use your value of m and the diameter of the wire, d, to determine a value for the resistivity, ρ, of the metal. Use $\rho = mA$ where A is the cross-sectional area of the wire.

4   Determine the uncertainty in your values for the gradient and A. Hence calculate the uncertainty in your value for the resistivity.

5   Find values for ρ from two different sources (one source should be online) and cite your research in an appropriate format. Compare these values with your calculated value of ρ and use the uncertainties you calculated to comment on your measurements.

6   Explain why your graph does not pass through the origin.

Questions

1 Explain how you might change the apparatus to calculate your value for the resistivity with greater resolution.

....

....

....

....

2 Explain why plotting a graph improves your accuracy.

....

....

....

....

3 a Explain why you need to use a wire to find the resistivity of a metal.

....

....

  b Explain what shape of sample would be suitable for a plastic.

....

....

....

4 Identify the sources of uncertainty in this experiment. Consider the accuracy (percentage difference) of your result and comment on the effect the uncertainties might have had.

....

....

....

....

....

5 Explain why the current through the wire should be small.

....

....

....

Plan

1 Plan a circuit to connect the following elements: cell, ammeter, voltmeter, and two resistors. One resistor, r, will act as internal resistance. The other resistor (the 100 Ω variable resistor) should be labelled R.

In your circuit:

- the cell and resistor r should be connected in series and used as a single circuit element
- you need to be able to measure the potential difference, V, across resistor R and the current, I, through it.

Draw your plan in the space below.

2 Comment on how you will make sure the equipment is used safely and continues to function properly.

3 Ask your teacher or technician to check and approve your circuit design, then set it up on the bench. Your circuit set-up should be checked again before you begin the experiment.

4 Vary the resistance of the variable resistor and record values for V and I. Take readings for the whole range of the variable resistor.

Objectives

- To make measurements using an electrical circuit

Equipment

- voltmeter on 2 V range
- ammeter on 200 mA range
- six leads to make electrical connections
- electrical cell such as a 1.5 V cell
- resistor to act as internal resistance
- 100 Ω variable resistor

Safety

- Provided a single cell (1.5 V battery) is used, the voltage and current will be non-hazardous.

Learning tip

- It is not usually necessary to repeat readings from an electrical circuit such as this. There is very little random error and very little judgement is required when taking readings. For this reason, you should take more than the usual six readings so you have more points on your graph. This will make it easier to recognise anomalies.

Results (Use this space to record your results.)

Analysis of results

The mathematical model for this circuit is $E - Ir = V$. Therefore, $V = -rI + E$.

1 Plot a graph of V against I. This should produce a straight line with gradient $-r$.

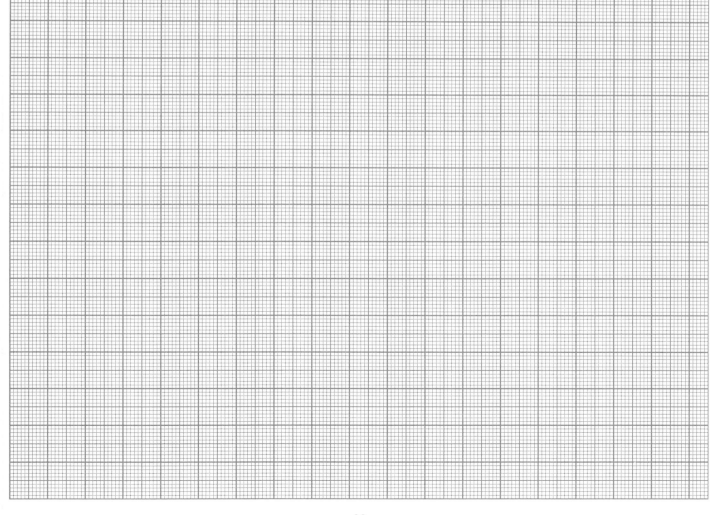

2 Find the gradient of your graph and compare it with the manufacturer's value of the resistor *r*. Remember to account for the powers of 10 (prefix) in the measured values for current.

3 Given that $E - Ir = V$, use your values of *r*, *V* and *I* to calculate *E*.

4 Justify the number of significant figures used in your answers to questions **2** and **3**.

5 Comment on the likely accuracy of your values for *E* and *r*.

Questions

1 When the internal resistance is large in comparison to the external resistance, the terminal potential difference falls to a small value. This is used to make high-voltage supplies safe for use in a laboratory. Explain how this makes the supply safe.

....

....

....

....

....

....

2 It should not matter whether the voltmeter is connected across R or across the cell. This is partly because of the low resistance of the ammeter. Explain why.

....

....

....

....

....

....

....

....

3 The intercept of your graph will be very close to the true value for the e.m.f. of the cell. Account for any difference.

....

....

....

....

4 Explain any difference between your value for r and the manufacturer's value.

....

....

Procedure

1 Secure the bench pulley to one end of the runway. This end of the runway should project over the end of a bench, so that the string connecting the mass hanger and the trolley passes over the pulley. The mass hanger will fall to the floor as the trolley moves along the runway. The runway should be tilted to compensate for friction.

2 Place the slotted mass hanger on the floor and move the trolley backwards along the runway until the string becomes tight, with the mass still on the floor. Place the light gate so it is positioned in the middle of the interrupt card on the trolley. There should be enough space on the ramp to allow the trolley to continue so that it clears the light gate before hitting the pulley.

3 Move the trolley further backwards until the mass hanger is touching the pulley. Put the five 10 g masses on the trolley so that they will not slide off. This is the start position for the experiment.

4 Record the total hanging mass, m. Release the trolley and use the stop clock to measure the time, T, it takes for the trolley to move from the start position to the light gate – this should be when the mass hanger hits the floor. Record the time reading, t, on the light gate. Repeat your measurements twice more and calculate mean values for T and t. Then estimate δT and δt, the uncertainties in these values.

5 Move one 10 g mass from the trolley to the hanger and repeat step **4**. Repeat this process, moving one 10 g mass at a time and recording m, T and t, until all of the masses are on the hanger.

6 Measure the combined mass, M, of the trolley, string, slotted masses and hanger.

7 Measure the distance, d, travelled by the trolley. This should be the same as the distance fallen by the mass hanger.

8 Record the length, L, of the card.

9 You can develop the investigation further by taking more readings after adding an additional mass, for example, 200 g, to the mass of the trolley.

Learning tip

● Choose a suitable scale for your graph so that your plot fills the whole page – you do not need to include the origin. This will make it easier to draw the last two gradient lines.

Objectives

● To determine the momentum change of a trolley when a force acts on it, as a function of time

Equipment

● five slotted masses (10 g) and hanger
● light gate and recorder
● stop clock
● metre rule
● dynamics trolley or air track vehicle
● runway or air track
● bench pulley
● string

⚠ Safety

● Runways and trolleys are very heavy and need to be placed so they will not slide or fall off benches.

● Air track blowers should be on the floor with the hose secured so that it cannot come loose and blow dust and dirt into people's faces.

● If large masses are used a catch box is needed in the drop zone to keep feet clear.

ORE PRACTICAL 9:
NVESTIGATE THE RELATIONSHIP BETWEEN THE FORCE EXERTED ON AN OBJECT
ND ITS CHANGE OF MOMENTUM

SPECIFICATION
REFERENCE

4.3.82

Results

1   Use this space to record your results. Remember to calculate the uncertainties in your values for T and t.

2   The force acting on the trolley is mg and this force acts for a time, T. The momentum of the trolley increases from zero to Mv, where v is the velocity of the trolley as it passes through the light gate.

Theory suggests that $mgT = Mv$.

For each set of values above, calculate $v = \dfrac{L}{t}$.

CORE PRACTICAL 9:
INVESTIGATE THE RELATIONSHIP BETWEEN THE FORCE EXERTED ON AN OBJECT
AND ITS CHANGE OF MOMENTUM

SPECIFICATION
REFERENCE

4.3.82

Analysis of results

1 Plot a graph of *mT* against *v*. This should give a straight line that passes through the origin.

CORE PRACTICAL 9:
INVESTIGATE THE RELATIONSHIP BETWEEN THE FORCE EXERTED ON AN OBJECT AND ITS CHANGE OF MOMENTUM

SPECIFICATION
REFERENCE

4.3.82

2 Find the gradient of your line of best fit and compare it with your value for $\frac{M}{g}$.

3 You can take the uncertainty in T and t as half the range of repeated readings. You need not work out the uncertainty for every value of T and t, but take typical values, neither the largest nor the smallest.

   a Calculate δv, the actual uncertainty in v, from the equation $\delta v = v\left(\frac{\delta t}{t}\right)$. Use a mid-range value for v.

   b Calculate $\delta(mT)$ by multiplying a mid-range value for m (for example, 30 g) by δT.

   c Use these actual uncertainties to draw error bars in both directions to form error boxes on your graph. Draw one line that is steeper than the line of best fit (LoBF) and one line that is less steep than the LoBF. Both of these lines should pass through the error boxes. Find the gradient of each new line.

The difference between the two gradients of the lines gives you the uncertainty in your gradient and this uncertainty is based on your readings.

Your value for $\frac{M}{g}$ should lie between these two values if Newton's second law is operating.

Questions

1 Calculate the percentage uncertainty in your value for the gradient and comment on the validity of your result.

....

....

....

....

....

....

2 Explain how friction will affect your result.

....

....

....

....

3 Describe how you reduced the effect of friction in your experiment and use your results to comment on the success of your method.

....

....

....

....

....

....

4 Explain how you might develop the use of ICT in this experiment.

....

....

....

....

5 Describe how you might use your readings to investigate the law of conservation of energy.

....

....

....

Procedure

1 Measure the mass and the diameter of each sphere.

2 Set the table or drawing board at a slight angle and position one sphere so that it is resting against the upper edge of the ruler. This sphere should be stationary. Then roll the other sphere along the upper edge of the ruler, so that it collides with the stationary sphere. Set up several collisions like this, to familiarise yourself with the equipment and allow for calibration.

3 After sufficient rehearsal, set up the digital camera to record the collisions. Set the table or drawing board horizontally and, without using the ruler, roll one sphere into the second stationary sphere. This time, the collision is unlikely to remain in one dimension, and there will be three tracks to record: the track of the approaching sphere, and two tracks for the two spheres after the collision.

4 Repeat, varying the line of approach so you can observe a variety of collision angles. You may wish to mark the graph paper or dressmaking paper where the stationary sphere is placed, to allow for small variations in approach. With practice, you will be able to use spheres of different diameters.

5 Use *Tracker* to analyse the video clips. Download the video files from the camera to the computer that runs *Tracker*, then load each clip into the program.

  Use the 'velocity overlay' feature so that the software can analyse the velocities of the spheres. You will need to multiply the velocity of each sphere by the mass if you wish to analyse the momentum.

6 You will need to keep a record of your work – you may wish to:
  - keep a digital file
  - print out and annotate screenshots from the *Tracker* program
  - draw the diagrams on paper and annotate them clearly and correctly.

Learning tip

- You will need to be able to use the sine and cosine functions to calculate components.

Objectives

- To investigate the conservation of momentum in two dimensions
- To determine whether a collision is elastic

Equipment

- small spheres (it is helpful to have spheres of two different diameters)
- digital camera able to record video
- computer with *Tracker* installed
- ruler
- micrometer or callipers
- means of controlling collision between two spheres
- support for camera vertically above the collision
- mass balance
- graph paper or dressmaking paper

⚠ Safety

- The masses and energies in this practical are low.
- The digital/video camera must be securely fixed so that it cannot fall on anyone.

Analysis of results

1 It is probably easiest to lay the x-axis along the path of the incoming sphere. Then, the components in the x-direction and the y-direction are the maximum and zero, respectively.

2 You will need to measure velocities as vectors, with both magnitude and direction, so it is very important to measure angles accurately.

3 Analyse the tracks to see if momentum is conserved along the line of the approach and perpendicular to that line.

4 Construct a momentum vector triangle and see if it closes (meaning momentum is conserved). You can also use a vector triangle to consider the energy involved in the collisions. When kinetic energy is conserved, you should find that there is a right angle between the two spheres after the collision (so long as the target sphere was stationary and the spheres have the same mass).

Results (Use this space to record your results or attach annotated screenshots from the *Tracker* program.)

Questions

1   Estimate the uncertainties in your calculated values.

2   Describe any difficulties you encountered in measuring the data.

....

....

....

....

....

....

....

....

....

....

CORE PRACTICAL 11:
USE AN OSCILLOSCOPE OR DATA LOGGER TO DISPLAY AND ANALYSE THE POTENTIAL DIFFERENCE (p.d.) ACROSS A CAPACITOR AS IT CHARGES AND DISCHARGES THROUGH A RESISTOR

Procedure

Part A: Charging

1   Set up your circuit as shown in Figure A. The voltmeter should read zero when the capacitor is uncharged.

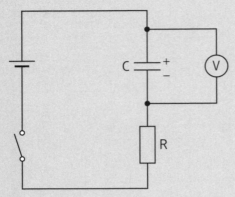

Figure A: Circuit set-up for Part A

2   To charge the capacitor, close the switch. Record the voltage at 5-second intervals as the capacitor charges.

3   Repeat step **2** using different resistors and capacitors.

Results (Use this space to record your results.)

CORE PRACTICAL 11:

USE AN OSCILLOSCOPE OR DATA LOGGER TO DISPLAY AND ANALYSE THE POTENTIAL DIFFERENCE (p.d.) ACROSS A CAPACITOR AS IT CHARGES AND DISCHARGES THROUGH A RESISTOR

SPECIFICATION REFERENCE

4.4.103

Graph (Plot a graph of p.d. across the capacitor against time.)

CORE PRACTICAL 11:
USE AN OSCILLOSCOPE OR DATA LOGGER TO DISPLAY AND ANALYSE THE POTENTIAL DIFFERENCE (p.d.) ACROSS A CAPACITOR AS IT CHARGES AND DISCHARGES THROUGH A RESISTOR

SPECIFICATION
REFERENCE

4.4.103

Part B: Measuring the time constant

1 Use the multimeter to measure the value of the resistor, R.

2 Use the oscilloscope to measure a value for the e.m.f. of the battery. If you are using a PSU, set the output to 6 V, and record the output potential difference (p.d.). Adjust the time base control of the oscilloscope until a continuous horizontal line is seen. It will be helpful if this lines up with the lowest horizontal line on the screen. The height of this line gives the voltage when the scale is taken into account. Adjust the vertical scale so that 6 V is close to the top of the screen and check the calibration of the screen.

3 Set up the circuit shown in Figure B, using the 100 μF capacitor, the 470 kΩ resistor, and the oscilloscope as the voltmeter.

4 Move the switch or the flying lead so that the capacitor, C, charges up and record the potential difference when charged as V_0.

5 Move the switch or the flying lead so that the capacitor begins to discharge and at the same time start the stop clock.

6 Use the lap timer facility on the stop clock to record the time taken for the potential difference to fall to a pre-determined value. For example, you could record the time taken for the voltage to fall from V_0 to 5 V, then 4 V, then 3.5 V and so on. If you cannot write down the results quickly enough, record the time for the first fall, then recharge the capacitor to V_0 and time the fall to the second pre-determined potential difference. You should repeat all of your readings.

Figure B: Circuit set-up for Part B

7 Take sufficient readings to enable you to plot a graph of the results and calculate the time constant for the discharge.

Learning tips

- The rate of discharge depends on how much charge is left, so the discharge is exponential according to the formula $V = V_0 e^{\frac{-t}{RC}}$. Taking logs to the base e of each side gives
$\ln V = \ln V_0 + \frac{-t}{RC}$. This is similar to $y = mx + c$.

- You can draw error bars on your graph to help you with uncertainties. You have found the uncertainty in your measurements of the time, δt. Use a mid-range value for t and determine the range of repeated readings for that value of t. This range becomes the length of the error bar which you can then apply to each plot.

- The tolerance on the value of the capacitor – often 20% – is not a measurement uncertainty.

Results (Use this space to record your results.)

CORE PRACTICAL 11:
USE AN OSCILLOSCOPE OR DATA LOGGER TO DISPLAY AND ANALYSE THE POTENTIAL DIFFERENCE (p.d.) ACROSS A CAPACITOR AS IT CHARGES AND DISCHARGES THROUGH A RESISTOR

SPECIFICATION REFERENCE

4.4.103

Analysis of results: Part B

1   Use your repeat readings to estimate the uncertainty in your values for time.

2   Plot a graph of $\ln V$ against t. This should produce a straight line graph with gradient $-\dfrac{1}{RC}$.

3   Find the gradient of your graph and use it to calculate a value for the time constant, RC.

4   Draw a second line of fit and use it to calculate a second value for the time constant. Then estimate the uncertainty in your value.

CORE PRACTICAL 11:
USE AN OSCILLOSCOPE OR DATA LOGGER TO DISPLAY AND ANALYSE THE POTENTIAL DIFFERENCE
(p.d.) ACROSS A CAPACITOR AS IT CHARGES AND DISCHARGES THROUGH A RESISTOR

SPECIFICATION
REFERENCE

4.4.103

5 Use your value for the time constant to calculate a value for the capacitance, C, and compare this value with the stated value of the capacitor. Consider your uncertainty to conclude whether the capacitor is within its tolerance.

Part C: Changing the value of the resistor

1 Set the alternating square wave supply (PSU) to deliver a 50 Hz square wave at 3 V and connect it to the oscilloscope. Adjust the controls to display the square wave. Disconnect the oscilloscope but do not vary the settings you have used to display the square wave.

2 Connect the PSU in series with a 5 μF capacitor and a 1.2 kΩ resistor. Connect the oscilloscope across the resistor so that it will read the potential difference across it – this also indicates the current in the circuit.

3 Sketch the trace you see on the oscilloscope and include voltage and time scales as axes.

4 Turn off the square wave supply and replace the 1.2 kΩ resistor with a 470 Ω resistor. Turn on the square wave supply and sketch the trace you see on the oscilloscope including voltage and time scales as axes.

CORE PRACTICAL 11:
USE AN OSCILLOSCOPE OR DATA LOGGER TO DISPLAY AND ANALYSE THE POTENTIAL DIFFERENCE (p.d.) ACROSS A CAPACITOR AS IT CHARGES AND DISCHARGES THROUGH A RESISTOR

SPECIFICATION REFERENCE

4.4.103

5 Repeat step 4 above but replace the resistor with a 2.2 kΩ resistor.

Learning tips

● When using unfamiliar equipment, such as an oscilloscope, it is a good idea to make various adjustments to establish how to use the controls and to familiarise yourself with the device. Do this before using it to make measurements.

Analysis of results: Part C

1 Use your sketches to explain the effect on the discharge of changing the resistance.

2 Use your sketches to estimate the time constant for each combination of capacitor and resistor.

CORE PRACTICAL 11:
USE AN OSCILLOSCOPE OR DATA LOGGER TO DISPLAY AND ANALYSE THE POTENTIAL DIFFERENCE (p.d.) ACROSS A CAPACITOR AS IT CHARGES AND DISCHARGES THROUGH A RESISTOR

SPECIFICATION REFERENCE

4.4.103

Questions

1 The values printed on resistors and capacitors are known as 'nominal values'. What does this mean?

....

....

....

....

2 Explain why the technique suggested for measuring the time is likely to reduce your uncertainties.

....

....

3 Give one advantage of using an oscilloscope to measure a potential difference.

....

....

....

....

....

....

4 In Part B, you could have plotted a graph of V against t. Why does a graph of $\ln V$ against t produce a more accurate value?

....

....

....

....

....

....

Procedure

Research

1 Find out how fixed points are used in the construction of a temperature scale.

2 Find out how the resistance of a negative temperature coefficient (NTC) thermistor varies with temperature, and compare this to other thermometric properties.

3 Explain why temperature scales depend on the type of thermometer being used.

4 Use an appropriate format to cite all sources you refer to.

Objectives

- To research temperature scales
- To determine the temperature variation of a thermistor
- To design a potential divider circuit that can be used to control temperature

Equipment

- Bunsen burner, tripod, gauze and heatproof mat
- ice
- variable resistor
- thermistor
- ohmmeter
- alcohol thermometer
- beaker containing water
- power supply unit (PSU)

⚠ Safety

- Do not handle the mains lead, socket or plug for the power supply with wet hands.
- The beaker of water should be placed so that it cannot splash the power supply.
- Ensure the connecting leads do not get too near the Bunsen flame.
- Take care when taking readings when the water is near, or at, boiling point.
- The thermistor should not exceed its voltage rating.

Plan

Devise a plan to measure the resistance of a thermistor over the range 0–100 °C. Your plan should include a risk assessment and you should consider how you will make your results as accurate as possible. Record your plan in the space below.

Learning tip

- Thermal experiments can be very difficult to control due to the thermal inertia of the components. Measuring the temperature of the actual semiconductor rather than the temperature of the water therefore requires careful thought.

Results

Carry out your planned practical and record your results in the space below.

Analysis of results

Draw a graph to show the resistance of a thermistor in the range 0–100 °C.

The resistance, R, of a thermistor varies with absolute temperature, T, according to the formula

$$R = R_0\, e^{\left(\frac{b}{T}\right)} \quad \text{so} \quad \ln R = \frac{b}{T} + a \quad \text{where } a = \ln R_0$$

Plotting a graph of $\ln R$ against $\frac{1}{T}$ will produce a straight line. This will be easier to read accurately than a curve.

Design

1 Use your graph to help you design a potential divider circuit that uses your thermistor and a variable resistor. Your circuit should give an output of 3.0V at 40°C from a 6V DC supply.

2 Construct your circuit and test your design. To do this, set up the Bunsen burner, tripod, gauze and heatproof mat, then raise the temperature of the water in the beaker to 40°C (as measured by the alcohol thermometer). Measure the output voltage from your circuit using the ohmmeter.

Questions

1 Consider the uncertainty in your measurement of temperature during your practical, and comment on the outcome of your design.

....

....

....

....

....

....

2 State two ways in which you might improve your experiment – not your design.

....

....

....

....

....

3 Comment on how well your risk assessment worked, and describe any safety issues that arose as you were carrying out the experiment.

....

....

....

....

....

....

CORE PRACTICAL 13:
DETERMINE THE SPECIFIC LATENT HEAT OF A PHASE CHANGE

SPECIFICATION REFERENCE

5.3.127

Procedure

1 Place the ice in the funnel and allow the ice to warm up to 0 °C. You will need to catch the melted ice in a container.

2 Determine the mass, m_0, of the empty and dry beaker. Your calculations later will be easier if you use grams as the unit of mass throughout this practical.

3 Put approximately 100 cm³ of water in the beaker and determine the mass, m_1, of the beaker plus the water. Measure the temperature, θ_1, of the water.

4 Add approximately 20 g of ice at 0 °C to the beaker. Stir until the ice melts.

5 Record the lowest temperature, θ_2, reached by the ice and water mixture. This will occur as the last of the ice melts.

6 Determine the mass, m_2, of the beaker, plus water, plus melted ice.

Learning tip

- When quantities are subtracted, uncertainties have a much larger effect.

Results (Use this space to record your results.)

Objectives

- To determine the specific latent heat of ice by measuring the drop in temperature of water containing melting ice

Equipment

- thermometer and stirrer
- access to mass balance
- funnel, supported by retort stand
- approximately 50 g of crushed ice
- container to catch melted ice
- 250 cm³ beaker

⚠ Safety

- Clamp the thermometer carefully so that it cannot tip the beaker over and do not use it as a stirrer.
- Clear up any spilt ice or water on the floor to avoid slipping.

Analysis of results

1 Calculate the mass, m_w, of the water, where $m_w = m_1 - m_0$.

2 Calculate the mass, m_i, of the ice, where $m_i = m_2 - m_1$.

3 Assume that the temperature of the ice when it was added to the water was $0\,°C$.
   The specific heat capacity, c, of water is $4.20\,J\,g^{-1}\,°C^{-1}$.

   To calculate the specific latent heat, L, of ice, consider the heat balance where:

   heat lost by cooling water = heat gained by ice and warming melted ice

   $$m_w \times c \times (\theta_1 - \theta_2) = (m_i \times L) + (m_i \times c \times (\theta_2 - 0))$$

   Calculate a value for L.

4 Discuss how successful you were when measuring a value for L, and describe how you might improve your method.

....

....

....

....

....

....

....

....

Questions

1   Consider the uncertainty in your measurement of temperature and comment on the outcome of your experiment.

....

....

....

....

....

2   Explain why it is important that the ice is melting before it is put into the beaker.

....

....

....

3   Explain why it is important that the ice is crushed so that it melts quickly.

....

....

....

....

....

4   Explain the effect of any heat gained from the room on your value for L.

....

....

....

....

....

Research and planning

1 Research the apparatus used to investigate Boyle's law and find out how it is used in practice.

2 Plan an investigation into Boyle's law, including two precautions you will take to improve accuracy. Record your plan in the space below.

3 Produce a risk assessment for your investigation. Add this to your plan.

Learning tip

- Boyle's law tells us that the pressure, p, and volume, V, are related by the expression $p \times V = $ constant.

Objectives

- To measure the volume of a gas at constant temperature but varying pressure

Equipment

- Boyle's law apparatus
- pressure pump
- safety screen

⚠ Safety

- Eye protection should be worn during all the time the apparatus is under pressure.
- Connections between the pump and the apparatus must be secure to avoid oil escaping at high pressure.
- Skin contact with oil that has leaked out should be avoided.

Results

Use the Boyle's law apparatus and your plan to carry out your investigation safely. Record your results in the space below.

CORE PRACTICAL 14:
INVESTIGATE THE RELATIONSHIP BETWEEN PRESSURE AND VOLUME OF A GAS AT
FIXED TEMPERATURE

SPECIFICATION
REFERENCE

5.3.131

Analysis of results

1 If possible, use ICT to display your data as a straight-line graph and attach your graph in the space below.
   If you do not have access to graphing software, plot a graph of your results in the space below.

2 Use your graph to calculate the value of the constant in Boyle's law.

3 Estimate the uncertainty in your value for the constant.

4 Discuss how successful your precautions were in improving accuracy.

CORE PRACTICAL 14:
INVESTIGATE THE RELATIONSHIP BETWEEN PRESSURE AND VOLUME OF A GAS AT FIXED TEMPERATURE

Questions

1   Describe the precautions you took to improve the accuracy of your measurements and explain how they worked.

....

....

....

....

....

....

2   Describe any safety hazards you identified and explain how your safety precautions worked in practice.

....

....

....

....

....

....

....

....

....

....

....

....

3   Describe how you observed the level of the oil when recording the volume.

....

....

4   Explain why it is sufficient to measure the length of the oil column and not the volume of the air directly.

....

....

....

Research

Research the rules for handling radioactive materials in schools and the practices required for safety. Record your findings in the space below, citing all sources of information in an appropriate format.

Planning

Write a plan for the safe conduct of an experiment to investigate the absorption of gamma radiation by lead. You should describe carefully how you will take readings, and how you will use these readings to calculate the count rate.

Objectives

- To measure the count rate when different thicknesses of lead are placed between a source of gamma radiation and a detector
- To determine the half-thickness of lead for gamma rays of a particular energy

Equipment

- source of gamma radiation and handling tools
- GM tube and counter
- bench apparatus to support source and GM tube
- stop clock
- sheets of lead
- micrometer or callipers

⚠ Safety

- Radioactive sources must be kept in their containers until needed and replaced as soon as the practical work is finished.
- A source must be handled with a long pair of forceps or a similar tool.
- The end of the source emitting the radiation must always point down and away from the body and never viewed directly.

Results

Once your plan has been checked and approved by a teacher or technician, carry out your experiment, making sure you work safely at all times. Use this space to record your results.

Learning tip

- Choose scales for your graph carefully, to make sure the plotted points fill more than half of the paper along both axes. Remember, your graph does not have to include the origin.

Analysis of results

A constant fraction of the radiation is absorbed for each thickness, x, of absorber, so the rate of absorption is exponential. This means that the measured count rate, C, will vary according to the formula $C = C_0 e^{-\mu x}$.

Taking logs to the base e of each side gives $\ln(C) = -\mu x + \ln(C_0)$ which is similar to $y = mx + c$. The value of the gradient will be $-\mu$, which is a constant, so the line should be straight with a constant negative gradient.

The half-thickness is the thickness of lead that reduces the count rate to half the initial count.

1 Plot a graph of your results.

2 The half-thickness is the thickness of lead that reduces the count rate to half the initial rate. Use your graph to determine the half-thickness of lead for the source used.

3 Estimate the uncertainty in your readings and draw error bars on your plots. Use your error bars to draw two more lines of best fit (one steeper than the original line, one less steep). Use these lines to estimate the uncertainty in your value for the half-thickness.

Questions

1 Explain why you are safer the further away you stand from a source of gamma radiation.

2 Explain why repeating your readings will improve them.

3 The GM tube could be attached to a datalogger instead of a simple counter.
Discuss whether using a datalogger would improve your results.

CORE PRACTICAL 16:
DETERMINE THE VALUE OF AN UNKNOWN MASS USING THE RESONANT FREQUENCIES
OF THE OSCILLATION OF KNOWN MASSES

SPECIFICATION
REFERENCE

5.5.149

Research and planning

1 A spring obeys Hooke's law, $F = kx$, where F is the force applied and x is the consequent extension. When a mass, m, is hung on a spring, it is related to the extension by $m = \dfrac{kx}{g}$. When the mass is pulled down and released, it oscillates with a resonant period, T. Find an expression relating m and T.

2 Plan an investigation in which you will measure the period of resonant oscillations of a range of known masses and use your results to determine the magnitude of an unknown mass, m. Record your plan in the space below.

Learning tip

- You could ask your teacher to tell you the approximate magnitude (to one significant figure) of the unknown mass, so you can plan a suitable range of readings.

Objectives

- To measure the resonant frequency of masses on a spring
- To use a graph of the results to determine an unknown mass by measuring its resonant frequency when on the spring

Equipment

- spring
- slotted masses and hanger
- retort stand with bosses and clamps
- stop clock
- unknown mass
- mass balance

⚠ Safety

- The stand holding the spring needs to be firmly clamped in place.
- The spring should be attached securely rather than simply hung on a hook.
- The spring should not be overloaded so that it passes its elastic limit or breaks when oscillating.
- If large masses are used eye protection will be needed in case the spring snaps.
- A catch box in the drop zone will keep feet away from any falling masses.

CORE PRACTICAL 16:
DETERMINE THE VALUE OF AN UNKNOWN MASS USING THE RESONANT FREQUENCIES
OF THE OSCILLATION OF KNOWN MASSES

SPECIFICATION
REFERENCE

5.5.149

Results

Once your plan has been checked and approved by a teacher or technician, carry out your investigation. Record your results in the space below.

Analysis of results

1 If possible, use ICT to plot a graph of your results, then print your graph and attach it on the following page. If you do not have access to graphing software, plot a graph of your results in the space on the following page.

2 Use your graph to determine m.

3 Weigh the unknown mass and compare the weighed value with your answer to question **2**. Comment on the accuracy of this value compared with the uncertainty in your readings.

CORE PRACTICAL 16:
DETERMINE THE VALUE OF AN UNKNOWN MASS USING THE RESONANT FREQUENCIES OF THE OSCILLATION OF KNOWN MASSES

SPECIFICATION REFERENCE

5.5.149

Graph (Attach or plot a graph of your results here.)

CORE PRACTICAL 16:
DETERMINE THE VALUE OF AN UNKNOWN MASS USING THE RESONANT FREQUENCIES
OF THE OSCILLATION OF KNOWN MASSES

SPECIFICATION
REFERENCE

5.5.149

Questions

1 Explain the techniques you used to improve the accuracy of your results for T.

....

....

....

2 Explain how a datalogger might be used to improve these readings and the effect it would have.

....

....

....

....

....

....

....

....

....

3 Explain the difference between free and forced oscillations.

....

....

....

....

....

....

Core Practical 1

- Use ratios, fractions and percentages (k here is the measurement you make).

  Percentage uncertainty (%U) = $\left(\dfrac{\text{uncertainty}}{\text{mean value}}\right) \times 100\%$

  Percentage difference (%D) = $\dfrac{(k - g)}{g} \times 100\%$

- Find arithmetic means.

  The mean of a range of data = $\dfrac{\text{sum of readings}}{\text{number of readings}}$

- Translate information between graphical, numerical and algebraic forms.
- Plot two variables from experimental or other data.
- Understand that $y = mx + c$ represents a linear relationship.
- Determine the slope and intercept of a linear graph.

Core Practical 2

- At terminal velocity, the vector sum of the forces on the ball is zero.

  weight − drag − upthrust = 0

- From this it can be shown that $\eta = \dfrac{2r^2 g(\rho - \sigma)}{9v}$, where η is the viscosity of the liquid, r is the radius of the ball, ρ is the density of the ball, σ is the density of the liquid and v is the terminal velocity.
- The percentage uncertainty in r^2 is double the percentage uncertainty in r. The percentage uncertainties in the densities should be small enough to ignore.
- Recognise and make use of appropriate units in calculations.
- Recognise and use expressions in decimal and standard form.
- Use ratios, fractions and percentages.
- Use an appropriate number of significant figures.
- Find arithmetic means, identify uncertainties in measurements and use simple techniques to determine uncertainty when data are combined by addition, subtraction, multiplication, division and raising to powers.
- Substitute numerical values into algebraic equations using appropriate units for physical quantities.

Core Practical 3

- $E = \dfrac{\sigma}{\varepsilon}$ where $\sigma = \dfrac{mg}{A}$

  Remember to use the radius when calculating the cross-sectional area, A, of the wire.

  m is the mass added.

- $\varepsilon = \dfrac{x}{L}$
- Recognise and make use of appropriate units in calculations.
- Recognise and use expressions in decimal and standard form.
- Use an appropriate number of significant figures.
- Change the subject of an equation, including non-linear equations.
- Substitute numerical values into algebraic equations using appropriate units for physical quantities.
- Translate information between graphical, numerical and algebraic forms.
- Plot two variables from experimental or other data.
- Understand that $y = mx + c$ represents a linear relationship.
- Determine the slope and intercept of a linear graph.

Core Practical 4

- $v = f \times \lambda$ and $f = \frac{1}{T}$ where T is the period of one complete oscillation. You can measure this from the oscilloscope screen.
- Recognise and make use of appropriate units in calculations.
- Use ratios, fractions and percentages.
- Use an appropriate number of significant figures.
- Find arithmetic means.
- Identify uncertainties in measurements and use simple techniques to determine uncertainty when data are combined by addition, subtraction, multiplication, division and raising to powers.
- Substitute numerical values into algebraic equations using appropriate units for physical quantities.

Core Practical 5

- $v = f\lambda$ and $v^2 = \frac{T}{\mu}$, so $f^2\lambda^2 = \frac{T}{\mu}$
- Use ratios, fractions and percentages.
- Use an appropriate number of significant figures.
- Find arithmetic means.
- Identify uncertainties in measurements and use simple techniques to determine uncertainty when data are combined by addition, subtraction, multiplication, division and raising to powers.
- Substitute numerical values into algebraic equations using appropriate units for physical quantities.
- Translate information between graphical, numerical and algebraic forms.
- Plot two variables from experimental or other data.
- Understand that $y = mx + c$ represents a linear relationship.
- Determine the slope and intercept of a linear graph.

Core Practical 6

- $n\lambda = d\sin\theta$, where $\sin\theta$ can be derived from $\tan\theta = \frac{s}{D}$ and s is the distance between maxima.

  d is the distance between adjacent slits so $d = \frac{1}{N}$ where N is the number of slits per metre.

- Recognise and make use of appropriate units in calculations.
- Recognise and use expressions in decimal and standard form.
- Use calculators to handle $\sin x$, $\cos x$ and $\tan x$ when x is expressed in degrees or radians.
- Use an appropriate number of significant figures.
- Find arithmetic means.
- Change the subject of an equation, including non-linear equations.
- Substitute numerical values into algebraic equations using appropriate units for physical quantities.
- Use angles in regular 2D and 3D structures.
- Use sin, cos and tan in physical problems.

Core Practical 7

- Given $\rho = \frac{RA}{l}$ where ρ and A are constant, a graph of R against l should be a straight line through the origin.
- Recognise and use expressions in decimal and standard form.
- Use ratios, fractions and percentages.
- Use an appropriate number of significant figures.
- Identify uncertainties in measurements and use simple techniques to determine uncertainty when data are combined by addition, subtraction, multiplication, division and raising to powers.

- Substitute numerical values into algebraic equations using appropriate units for physical quantities.
- Translate information between graphical, numerical and algebraic forms.
- Plot two variables from experimental or other data.
- Understand that $y = mx + c$ represents a linear relationship.
- Determine the slope and intercept of a linear graph.

Core Practical 8

- The mathematical model for this circuit is $E - Ir = V$.
- Recognise and make use of appropriate units in calculations.
- Use an appropriate number of significant figures.
- Identify uncertainties in measurements and use simple techniques to determine uncertainty when data are combined by addition, subtraction, multiplication, division and raising to powers.
- Translate information between graphical, numerical and algebraic forms.
- Plot two variables from experimental or other data.
- Understand that $y = mx + c$ represents a linear relationship.
- Determine the slope and intercept of a linear graph.

Core Practical 9

- Recognise and make use of appropriate units in calculations.
- Use ratios, fractions and percentages.
- Use an appropriate number of significant figures.
- Identify uncertainties in measurements and use simple techniques to determine uncertainty when data are combined by addition, subtraction, multiplication, division and raising to powers.
- Translate information between graphical, numerical and algebraic forms.
- Plot two variables from experimental or other data.
- Understand that $y = mx + c$ represents a linear relationship.
- Determine the slope and intercept of a linear graph.

Useful equations:

- $F \triangle t = m \triangle v$ shows the impulse of a force is equal to the change in momentum.
- $y = mx + c$ shows why the intercept should be zero.

Core Practical 10

- Recognise and make use of appropriate units in calculations.
- Use calculators to handle $\sin x$, $\cos x$ and $\tan x$ when x is expressed in degrees or radians.
- Use an appropriate number of significant figures.
- Substitute numerical values into algebraic equations using appropriate units for physical quantities.
- Use angles in regular 2D and 3D structures.
- Use Pythagoras' theorem and the angle sum of a triangle.
- Use sin, cos and tan in physical problems.

Core Practical 11

- Recognise and make use of appropriate units in calculations.
- Recognise and use expressions in decimal and standard form.
- Use ratios, fractions and percentages.
- Use calculators to find and use power, exponential and logarithmic functions.
- Use an appropriate number of significant figures.

- Identify uncertainties in measurements and use simple techniques to determine uncertainty when data are combined by addition, subtraction, multiplication, division and raising to powers.
- Substitute numerical values into algebraic equations using appropriate units for physical quantities.
- Use logarithms in relation to quantities that range over several orders of magnitude.
- Translate information between graphical, numerical and algebraic forms.
- Plot two variables from experimental or other data.
- Understand that $y = mx + c$ represents a linear relationship.
- Determine the slope and intercept of a linear graph.
- Interpret logarithmic plots.
- Use logarithmic plots to test exponential and power law variations.

Core Practical 12

- Recognise and make use of appropriate units in calculations.
- Use ratios, fractions and percentages.
- Use calculators to find and use power, exponential and logarithmic functions.
- Use an appropriate number of significant figures.
- Identify uncertainties in measurements and use simple techniques to determine uncertainty when data are combined by addition, subtraction, multiplication, division and raising to powers.
- Substitute numerical values into algebraic equations using appropriate units for physical quantities.
- Use logarithms in relation to quantities that range over several orders of magnitude.
- Translate information between graphical, numerical and algebraic forms.
- Plot two variables from experimental or other data.
- Understand that $y = mx + c$ represents a linear relationship.
- Determine the slope and intercept of a linear graph.
- Interpret logarithmic plots.
- Use logarithmic plots to test exponential and power law variations.

Core Practical 13

- Recognise and make use of appropriate units in calculations.
- Use ratios, fractions and percentages.
- Use an appropriate number of significant figures.
- Identify uncertainties in measurements and use simple techniques to determine uncertainty when data are combined by addition, subtraction, multiplication, division and raising to powers.
- Change the subject of an equation, including non-linear equations.
- Substitute numerical values into algebraic equations using appropriate units for physical quantities.

Core Practical 14

- Recognise and make use of appropriate units in calculations.
- Use ratios, fractions and percentages.
- Use an appropriate number of significant figures.
- Identify uncertainties in measurements and use simple techniques to determine uncertainty when data are combined by addition, subtraction, multiplication, division and raising to powers.
- Substitute numerical values into algebraic equations using appropriate units for physical quantities.
- Translate information between graphical, numerical and algebraic forms.
- Plot two variables from experimental or other data.
- Understand that $y = mx + c$ represents a linear relationship.

- Determine the slope and intercept of a linear graph.
- Sketch relationships which are modelled by $y = \dfrac{k}{x}$, $y = kx^2$, $y = \dfrac{k}{x^2}$, $y = kx$, $y = \sin x$, $y = \cos x$, $y = e^{\pm x}$, $y = \sin^2 x$, and $y = \cos^2 x$ as applied to physical relationships.

Core Practical 15

- Recognise and make use of appropriate units in calculations.
- Use calculators to find and use power, exponential and logarithmic functions.
- Use an appropriate number of significant figures.
- Find arithmetic means.
- Understand simple probability.
- Substitute numerical values into algebraic equations using appropriate units for physical quantities.
- Use logarithms in relation to quantities that range over several orders of magnitude.
- Translate information between graphical, numerical and algebraic forms.
- Plot two variables from experimental or other data.
- Understand that $y = mx + c$ represents a linear relationship.
- Determine the slope and intercept of a linear graph.
- Interpret logarithmic plots.
- Use logarithmic plots to test exponential and power law variations.

Core Practical 16

- Recognise and make use of appropriate units in calculations.
- Use ratios, fractions and percentages.
- Use calculators to find and use power, exponential and logarithmic functions.
- Use an appropriate number of significant figures.
- Find arithmetic means.
- Identify uncertainties in measurements and use simple techniques to determine uncertainty when data are combined by addition, subtraction, multiplication, division and raising to powers.
- Change the subject of an equation, including non-linear equations.
- Substitute numerical values into algebraic equations using appropriate units for physical quantities.
- Translate information between graphical, numerical and algebraic forms.
- Plot two variables from experimental or other data.
- Understand that $y = mx + c$ represents a linear relationship.

ANSWERS

Core Practical 1

1 There should be less uncertainty in the measurement of time; this will be of particular interest if students have used both methods.

2 Your value for g will have been reduced by air resistance. Answers should refer to the %D calculated during analysis of the results.

3 A straight line has a constant gradient. The line should be straight because the gradient depends only on g, which is constant.

Core Practical 2

1 The liquid is coloured and the low intensity of the light transmitted will make the timing unreliable. It is also likely that the ball will not fall through the relatively narrow beam of the light gate.

2 Bernoulli's principle means that, as the ball approaches the wall, the flow of the liquid is accelerated. Because of this, the pressure reduces and the ball moves closer to the wall, making any effect more pronounced. The streamlines for the flow will no longer be symmetrical and Stokes' law is unlikely to be an appropriate mathematical model.

3 Because time is measured at two intervals for each ball, it is possible to estimate the uncertainty in the calculated value of terminal velocity for each ball. Using balls of the same diameter will allow you to calculate a mean value for the terminal velocity of balls of that diameter. Thus, you can calculate a value for viscosity for each diameter of ball and use these values to find an overall mean value for the viscosity of the liquid.

The terminal velocity is likely to be the major source of uncertainty, since we are ignoring the uncertainty in the densities. In your answer, you should compare the percentage differences between your values for viscosity at different diameters and the calculated uncertainty from your measurements.

Core Practical 3

1 A long wire makes the extension large enough to read.

Since $x = \dfrac{FL}{AE}$, a large value for L and a small value for A make x large enough to measure with a metre rule.

2 Take pairs of readings at right angles to each other. This will reduce any uncertainty if the wire is not quite circular. Take repeat measurements down the length of the wire: five pairs of values should be sufficient. Calculate the mean of all 10 values.

3 The extension is very small and, using a metre rule, we can only measure to one significant figure. Our value of the Young modulus was calculated from a graph of mass added against extension, so we might trust two significant figures. However, one significant figure is strictly correct.

4 Answers will vary. Research involving the Young modulus of copper is easily accessible.

Core Practical 4

1 The trace on the screen can be quite thick, so there may be some uncertainty about where exactly to place the speaker each time. Similarly, the resolution of the screen measurement for the frequency is about 2 mm.

2 The percentage difference might be very small if the measurements are accurate. The percentage uncertainties are likely to be about 2% each. So this looks like an accurate result and is likely to be close to the true value on the day.

3 Since the x-axis displays time, we can tell that the sound is taking one extra period to travel from the speaker to the microphone. The distance travelled in one period is the wavelength.

4 We need a wavelength that can be measured to a good resolution using a metre rule.

Core Practical 5

1 This is likely to be the measurement of a resonant frequency, unless the calibration of the signal generator is accurate. There will also be uncertainty in the measurement of the wavelength, because a thick blur is observed at the nodes.

2 Your description should refer to control variables and give some reasons for the values and ranges selected.

3 The sharpness of resonance is likely to cause problems. Adjusting the frequency while looking closely at the node should allow you to observe the largest response. Looking at the amplitude is likely to be less helpful.

4 Answers will vary. Research involving resonant cavities for lasers and radio frequency waves is easily accessible. You might like to research the history of this measurement as well.

Core Practical 6

1 Laser light is monochromatic, so the maximum is small. It is also coherent, so the maximum is produced without further focusing. The light is bright and a large value for D can be used without the maxima becoming too dim to see properly.

2 A resolution of 1 mm is suitable when measuring distances of around 70 cm (for the 300 slits/mm grating) and around 25 cm (for the 100 slits/mm grating) because this gives percentage uncertainties of 0.1% and 0.4%, respectively.

3 White light is a mixture of frequencies, so the diffraction would be different for each frequency. The maxima are small so, in practice, the inner edge would be blue-ish and the outer edge would be red-ish.

Core Practical 7

1 If you originally used a multimeter that reads to two significant figures, using a voltmeter and an ammeter that read to three significant figures will provide greater resolution.

2 It makes it easier to spot anomalies and is a good, quick way of finding a weighted average.

3 a The resistance is measurable and not very small.

   b For an insulator such as a plastic, the sample should be quite thick and fairly short so the resistance is measurable.

4 • Contact resistance between wire and plug

   • Resistance between crocodile clip and wire at 'zero' end of wire

   • Crocodile clip not at 'zero' mark

   All these uncertainties would shift the line of best fit up the graph without affecting the gradient, so the accuracy should be unaffected.

5 Resistivity is temperature dependent, so the wire must not be allowed to heat up. Keeping the current small will help with this.

Core Practical 8

1 If a human body is connected across the terminals, the resistance will be about 25 kΩ. If the internal resistance of the supply is 5 MΩ, the terminal potential difference falls to a low value with very little current flowing, making it safe.

2 The low resistance of the ammeter means that the potential difference across the ammeter will be very small; it is assumed to be so small that it can be ignored. This means that the potential difference across R and across the cell is the same.

3 The voltmeter does not have an infinite resistance. Any small current will cause a pd across the internal resistance, reducing the terminal pd below the e.m.f.

4 The cell itself has an internal resistance, but this is very small.

Core Practical 9

1 Calculate the difference between the gradients of the lines of fit. Then divide this difference by the gradient of the line of best fit and express the answer as a percentage.

The computed value for $\dfrac{M}{g}$ should lie within the uncertainty.

2 Friction will oppose the motion of the trolley, so the force acting on the trolley will be reduced, and the velocity at the light gate will be reduced. This will make the gradient smaller.

3 Answers may refer to:
- the use of an air track, where there is no contact but considerable air resistance
- a downward slope on the track, to compensate for the effects of friction. The slope should be adjusted so that the trolley, when pushed, runs at a constant speed.

The success of the method used can be judged in part by the percentage uncertainty calculated in question **1**.

4 You should consider how you could use the centre's apparatus more effectively. For example, you could discuss the use of a datalogger and multiple light gates.

5 You may consider the kinetic energy and calculate the transfer from gravitational potential energy as the mass falls.

Core Practical 10

1 Estimation of uncertainties can be based on variations in repeated readings where possible; otherwise the resolution of the measurements can be used.

2 Answers will vary.

Core Practical 11

1 This means the values may not be completely accurate, due to manufacturing tolerances which produce variance in the components produced.

2 The experimenter does not have to look at two screens at the same time.

3 The square wave is much quicker, so the values used can be much smaller. The oscilloscope also has a very high resistance, so it will not discharge the capacitor itself.

4 A graph of V against t would have produced an exponential decay curve. The graph you plotted – $\ln V$ against t – produces a straight line. This effectively averages several readings. It is also easier to gain further data from a straight line graph than from an exponential decay curve.

Core Practical 12

1 You should consider the percentage difference between your experimental and design values, and compare this with your estimate of the percentage uncertainty in temperature. You might also consider how straight your log graph is.

2 You should use the idea that heating very slowly will allow the temperature of the semiconductor to be close to that of the water, and hence the alcohol thermometer as well. With a longer time span, a datalogger with resistance and temperature probes will be very helpful and will improve accuracy.

3 You should consider how well you maintained safety as the temperature increased, for example, not only personal safety but also keeping the leads away from the hot gauze and supporting the thermometer.

Core Practical 13

1 The uncertainty in the temperature measurement is probably 0.5 °C. The uncertainty in a temperature difference is therefore 1 °C, since two temperatures are subtracted. Comments should reflect the outcome of the experiment, suggesting improvements where necessary.

2 The method does not account for any heat the ice will absorb as the temperature rises to 0 °C.

3 As long as the ice and water mixture is below room temperature, it will be absorbing heat from the room. If this time is minimised (by using crushed ice, which will melt more quickly), the error introduced by the heat gained from the room will be reduced.

4 Heat gained from the room will mean that there is more heat entering the ice on the left-hand side of the heat balance equation. As a result, the value for L will be too small. This is because the heat entering means that θ_2 is not as low as it might be (and $m_w > m_i$).

Core Practical 14

1 Answers may include the following:
- Carried out the pressure changes slowly and left some time between them so that the temperature of the gas was unaffected by the change in volume.
- Increased the pressure to give a decreasing volume. Could not decrease the pressure to obtain repeat readings because the oil would cling to the walls of the tube if the volume of gas increased, making the volume readings too large.

2 Possible hazards include the following:
- The apparatus could have fallen over.
- The pressure pump, with sufficient force, could have been unstable.
- The tubing or joints could have burst under the increased pressure.

The precautions taken may include the following:
- The apparatus was weighted or clamped to improve stability and the apparatus was not close to the edge of the bench.
- Care was taken when pressing on the pump, especially at high pressures, to make sure that the action was vertically down and above the base of the pump.
- No action could be taken to completely avoid the risk of the apparatus bursting at high pressure, but the apparatus was observed carefully as the work was carried out and safety goggles were worn by all.

3 Line-of-sight observation was made at the same horizontal level as the bottom of the meniscus. The reading was taken from the adjacent scale.

4 The air is contained above the oil and the length scale starts from the top of the column. The cross-section, A, of the tube is constant, so the volume, V, of air above the oil is proportional to the length, l, since $V = A \times l$. This practical seeks to establish proportionality so measuring the length of the oil column rather than the volume of air does not affect the result.

Core Practical 15

1 As gamma rays spread out, their intensity decreases according to the inverse square law, so doubling your distance from the source reduces your dose by 75%.

2 The decay is random and will naturally fluctuate over time. If you take repeated readings, you will be able to calculate an average; you can also estimate the uncertainty using the range of each set of repeats.

3 A datalogger would make it easier to calculate the rate, because most software programs can calculate this directly. However, the uncertainty in measuring the time by hand is very small and repeat readings are taken, so measurements from a datalogger are unlikely to be much more accurate because the datalogger will not be taking readings over a longer period of time. Other valid arguments should be considered.

Core Practical 16

1 Record multiple oscillations (for example, 10), repeat the reading and calculate a mean. Divide the mean by the number of oscillations.

2 You could place a position sensor under the mass hanger and connect it to the datalogger. This could then be used to measure the extension and the period.

If the resolution of the position sensor is 0.1 mm or higher, this is better than a metre rule. However, the method for measuring T described in question **1** is likely to have very small uncertainties (probably between 0.5% and 1%), so it is unlikely that the datalogger will improve measurements of T unless the time period is very small.

3 When a mass is displaced and released (as in this experiment), free oscillations take place. If energy is continually put into the system (for example, by moving the support up and down), the oscillation is forced. The system gains energy and, unless damped, is likely to break.